Fingerspelling
the
Real World

Suellen J. Bahleda

Real World Press
Eagle River, Alaska
©1996

Printed in the United States of America

ISBN 0-9651898-7-2

10 9 8 7 6 5 4 3 2 1

Real World Press
PO Box 771911
Eagle River, Alaska 99577

PREFACE

A great deal of mental energy is misused in relationship to fingerspelling. Too often, when a person you are communicating with begins to fingerspell, our mental message goes something like this: "Oh my gosh, (s)he's fingerspelling and that is my worst thing! I never get the fingerspelling! I am so bad at this! I hate it when people fingerspell! I am so dumb! I'll never be able to understand fingerspelling!"

By this time, the fingerspelled message has come and gone, and because you were so busy telling yourself you always miss this kind of thing, you have indeed missed it.

The goal of this book is twofold: to give you techniques and practice for your own fingerspelling, and to give you an understanding of the uses of fingerspelling within manual communication. These tools will enable you to approach fingerspelling with more confidence, allowing you to use your mental energy for communication, rather than for 'Oh, no!' messages.

Expressive fingerspelling is like learning to type, or to play the clarinet. Your hands have to memorize the way to get to the *z* on the keyboard, or the correct fingering for a b-flat. Practicing the movement and the stretch of those motions teaches your hand the correct feel and placement. After a while, your hands recognize the right way to make those practiced movements without your having to place them consciously.

Fingerspelling is much the same. Have you ever noticed when you fingerspell something incorrectly, you often make the same exact error on the second attempt? Your hand has already "memorized" the shape you made the first time! Practicing the shapes in this book is like practicing musical scales. Your hand must learn the feel of the shapes in differing configurations.

Thinking about fingerspelling based on combinations of shapes rather than letter-by-letter will positively affect the efficiency of your own fingerspelling, as well as give you a practical approach to reading another's fingerspelling.

Spell on!

My thanks to all the students and workshop participants who have allowed me to experiment on them, who have provided me with wonderful feedback, and who have participated in the joy of shared learning.

My heartfelt appreciation to Conny Katasse for her time and expertise in providing valuable suggestions and improvements.

My deepest thanks to these special people for their encouragement, support, mentorship, and faith:
Sam Busco, David Chapman, Julie Chapman. Lyn Stoller, the Billikin Club, Mom and Dad, Michael, and especially Bill.

This book is dedicated to a boy named Robert, my first fingerspelling partner, who didn't mind when I forgot x or q, or confused d and f, just as long as we talked.

TABLE OF CONTENTS

TABLE OF CONTENTS, continued

How to Use This Book

This book begins with a brief discussion of uses of fingerspelling within manual communication, expressive tips, and receptive tips. This is followed by a series of practice pages. Each practice page includes a root shape, expanded shapes, and embedded shapes.

Root shape

A N

Expanded shapes	Embedded shapes		
y a n	p a n d a	e v a n g e l i s t	B r i a n
i a n	T r a v a n t i	K a n s a s	t o b o g g a n
e a n	C u b a n	B u n y a n	J u a n
t a n	B l a n c h a r d	n a n n y	c a n c e r
v a n	D e a n	B h u t a n	f a n g s
g a n	o r e g a n o	B y z a n t i n e	r a n c i d
z a n	C a a n	v a n d a l	t u r b a n
l a n	T a r z a n	r a n c h	E v a n

The root shape is a combination that naturally occurs in fingerspelled items. The expanded shape further develops the combination. As you practice the expanded shapes, notice how the root shape adapts to accommodate the form which precedes or follows it. Embedded shapes incorporate the expanded shapes into complete fingerspelled words. The expanded shape may begin or end a word, or may be incorporated within the body of the word. Again, notice how the shape alters within the flow of the entire fingerspelled word.

> When working on fingerspelling, it is imperative that you pay attention to how physically taxing this can be in the beginning. Do a gentle stretching warm-up before beginning fingerspelling practice. Practicing these shapes requires you to move your hands and fingers in new ways. Practice only one or, at most, two shapes at a sitting. Be sure to stop and stretch out frequently.

Choose a shape to practice. Form that shape several times so your hand gets the "feel" of it. Then move into the expanded shapes. Form each one several times to allow your hand to learn how it needs to adapt the shape within that context. Move on to the next expanded shape when you are comfortable with the flow of each particular shape. When you are ready, begin working on the embedded shapes.

Practice a word from the list. Notice how the root shape feels within that context, how it adapts to the context.

Create an ASL sentence using that embedded shape word. Feel the flow from the sign preceding the embedded shape word and how the fingerspelling then flows into the sign following it.

Remember, fingerspelling does not occur in isolation. Deaf people will not walk up to you, flash a fingerspelled word at you, and walk away! Fingerspelling is always rooted in a context. Practice using fingerspelling as it naturally occurs, within a context.

Continue the process, working through the embedded shape list.

It is not important that you practice each and every word on the list at each and every sitting. Choose words that strike you, investigate words you may not know, note which ones especially challenge you. Are there local Deaf people, interpreters, teachers, street names, favorite restaurants, agencies that incorporate those shapes? Add them to the lists.

Notice that some words appear on multiple lists; every word incorporates multiple shapes.

As you develop expressive fluidity and confidence, you can work with a partner or study group to share receptive practice. Again, practice fingerspelling within a context. Don't just fingerspell lists of words to each other; discuss the weather, debate a hot topic, have a conversation! Each list has starter suggestions, possible context ideas based on words from the list. The starters are just for fun; don't worry about being technically or historically accurate. Be inventive!

One other area of practice is included in this book: numeric practice. There are tips for signing times, dates, ages, addresses, phone numbers, and money, as well as practice lists for each topic. Be sure to practice these in context as well.

There is one thing this book does not have: pictures of what fingerspelled letters are supposed to look like. There are many resources available that show the ideal frozen shape, but the best place to see fingerspelled shapes is in use! An *e* will look very different before an *s* compared to after an *n*, on long fingers, fat fingers, child fingers, even partial fingers!

To the Instructor

Fingerspelling the Real World is a manual designed to give students concentrated practice in fingerspelling, utilizing vocabulary that would be fingerspelled in real world settings. This manual will also build a foundation for the types of information that may be fingerspelled.

There are three discussion units in this manual: Uses of Fingerspelling Within Manual Communication, Receptive Tips, and Expressive Tips. These discussions are meant to be used as overviews to generate class discussion. Your examples, including names and places from your local community, are invaluable in showing application to the "real world."

The 2,300+ practice items are divided into 30 shape-based lesson units. It is not necessary to follow the book in sequence; the 'Shape of the Day' can be randomly selected. You may wish to create flashcards using the word lists to introduce the shape and get the students warmed up before turning to the book. It is recommended that no more than two shapes be introduced in any one lesson.

Be sure to have students stretch out before begining concentrated practice. You may wish to periodically stop and have them do gentle stretches during the lesson.

Each unit includes starters: story and paragraph ideas generated from vocabulary from the shape list. These are designed to encourage students to put fingerspelling within a context, rather than just fingerspelling word list after word list. Students are encouraged to create their own starters; these short stories are ideal for videotaping and feedback.

Also included in this manual are brief discussions and practice lists for a variety of numeric topics: money, time, age, dates, addresses, and telephone numbers. You may wish to use flashcards for supplemental practice. Flashcards for numeric topics such as time, money, and basic numeric practice are available at many teacher supply stores.

Standard board games such as Battleship, Trivial Pursuit, and Memory Madness are great for break-out practice sessions. Also consider using local restaurant menus and mail order catalogues for practice incorporating numbers. An endless source of practice material is a collection of business cards; students can practice first and last names, company names, addresses, zip codes, and phone numbers from these.

It is important to incorporate fingerspelled and numeric information in ASL sentences for testing/evaluation. Do not fingerspell isolated vocabulary items for testing/evaluation purposes, as this does not reflect what happens in the real world.

A practical tip : If a student's elbows start to wander too high, loop an ACE bandage around his/her waist, and a second loop around his/her upper arm. This allows the student a natural range of motion, but when the elbow starts to rise, the tug of the bandage reminds him/her to keep it at waist level.

Use of Fingerspelling Within Manual Communication

What information is fingerspelled, and why? Often, in our mental panic approach to fingerspelling, the fingerspelled messages bombard us with no apparent rhyme or reason. However, there *are* specific uses of fingerspelling within American Sign Language. Knowing there are reasons for using a fingerspelled item helps in our approach to a fingerspelled message.

Types of fingerspelled information fall into three main categories: proper names, technological-/profession- based words, and clarification.

> Proper names include:
> - people's names
>   Mr. Coyle, Hazel, Richard
> - place names
>   Wrigley Field, Lakewood, Main Street
> - titles of books, movies, TV shows, and magazines
>   Deaf Heritage, Ben-Hur, Roseanne, Newsweek

> Technological information includes:
> - science and medical-bound words
>   petri dish, brontosaurus, chemotherapy
> - profession-specific terminology
>   byte, spitball, mutual fund, gesso

> Clarification is done through two types of redundancy:
> -to specify a particular word for a sign with
> multiple gloss synonyms
> > sign BEAUTIFUL with fingerspelled
> >   clarification A-T-T-R-A-C-T-I-V-E
> > sign FISH with fingerspelled specification
> > S-A-L-M-O-N
> -to present a concept in multiple modes
> > sign DORM plus D-O-R-M

This use of redundancy is often confusing to beginning signers who complain they understood the sign, but missed the fingerspelling after it!

Recognizing that fingerspelling occurs within these contexts helps to narrow the focus of seemingly random fingerspelled items int a logical inclusion. Most fingerspelling can be accounted for e three main categories of uses. *Most* fingerspelling.

There is one use of fingerspelling that is not bou ree contexts. It is one in which you have no contr context can be called, "Just Because." Often a signe ell a word that has a commonly known/used sign. because of the flow of a particular sentence, becau s family/residential school peers always fingerspelled it, e it fit the signer's mood at that particular moment.

Many beginning signers get stuck on the fingerspelled C-A-R. When they finally get it, after having struggled mightily to figure out what in the heck that short fingerspelled blur was, they have two thoughts. The first is, "Oh my gosh, if I couldn't understand a dinky little word like 'car' I will never get fingerspelling.", followed by an irate "Why did she fingerspell it anyway? I would have gotten it if she had just used the sign!" Fear not; you *will* get fingerspelling, and welcome to the world of "Just Because."

Receptive Tips

✔ Accept that there will be times when you will not immediately understand a fingerspelled piece of information. No one is expected to understand every piece of fingerspelling every time.

✔ Realize there is as much individuality in fingerspelling as in penmanship.

✔ Remember your context. If you are speaking with a person about his ailing grandmother, and you see A-L-Z-something-something-something, you have enough to come up with Alzheimer's Disease.

✔ Asking the signer to slow down doesn't help and doesn't work. People speak and sign at their own natural pace. Asking them to slow down will only be momentarily effective, as they will quickly return to their regular pace. Slowed fingerspelling also feeds the temptation to try to decode the word letter by letter, rather than using shapes, movements and context.

✔ If you need to question the signer, ask questions which reflect your understanding up to that point: YOUR NEPHEW NAME? or S-H-A ... WHAT? lets the signer know you were following the message, and what specific parts need clarification. Statements like "I missed the fingerspelling" reinforces negative perceptions of your abilities on both your and your signing partner's part.

✔ Wait. Too often the signer is interrupted before having finished fingerspelling the word! Allow the signer to complete the fingerspelling, because you may see enough information to fill in the gaps. Even better, wait a few signs beyond the fingerspelling for more context. Often, important fingerspelled information is repeated further along in the message, giving you a second chance to get the complete message.

✔ Give yourself credit for the pieces you *did* see, and use those clues. Was it a long word, a short word? Were there movements which tip off p,q,j,z? Did you catch the first letter? The last? What's the context? Often putting together "the parts" will result in a "whole!"

✔ Develop a positive mindset. Congratulate yourself for words you did get, rather than focusing on ones you missed. What did you do right?...Do it again!

✔ Make a value judgment. Asking the signer to repeat a fingerspelled portion over and over stops the flow of communication, and becomes an exercise in frustration for you both. Have the patience and confidence to look at the whole message, and to decide if that one fingerspelled element is crucial for overall understanding. Often, if it is an important fingerspelled item, it will be repeated in the conversation. Seeing it again, after having time to process it, helps the pieces come together. If it is not necessarily crucial to the understanding of the story, it probably won't come up again, and you can "skim" over it, as you would an unfamiliar vocabulary word in a newspaper article.

Expressive Tips

✔ Relax! Release tension in your fingers, wrist, elbow, and shoulder.

✔ Warm-up and stretch out before practicing.

✔ Keep your elbow close to your waist and your hand in the general shoulder area. This creates a natural background for fingerspelling.

✔ Don't fingerspell letter by letter. Success in fingerspelling requires the same type of skill you already have in English: the ability to recognize words as whole units rather than groups of letters. You should think *the word* as you fingerspell it, not the individual letters of that word.

✔ Don't cover your mouth. Many times fingerspelled words are also mouthed to add clarification.

✔ Practice to get the feel of the word. Your hand will memorize the feel of the shapes, just as a pianist's hands learn the feel of the fingering for an F# chord.

✔ Everyone makes spelling mistakes now and then. When it happens, do NOT slap your hand, shake it out, "erase," make a scene, etc. Doing those things interrupts the flow of your message. Either calmly start over, or simply sign "WRONG" and begin again.

✔ You don't need to be a perfect speller. Often the person you are communicating with "gets" the imperfectly spelled message through context. If it's apparent the message was understood, warts and all, then move on!

✔ Make your goal clarity, not speed. It doesn't matter how fast you can produce the message if no one understands it!

✔ Use appropriate ASL grammatical facial markers.

✔ For double letters, different methods including the slide (d→d), the bounce (d ⌒ d), and the tap (d∨∖d) are all used. Find which is most comfortable and efficient for you.

If you only read one thing in this book, read this:

Practice the shape of both your first and last names until your hand learns to "just do it." A beginning signer/fingerspeller often wishes a hole would open up and swallow her when she muffs the first thing she has to fingerspell when meeting new Deaf persons: her own name.

BU   *ow*

                                    pa

                Ng   *BE*

AY

        qu   CH

                bA

SHAPES

nX

                RU   to

eN   DE

        IN   *em*

                        gE

                TE

                        bu

ax

                                        IS

✍ **Your   additions/notes**

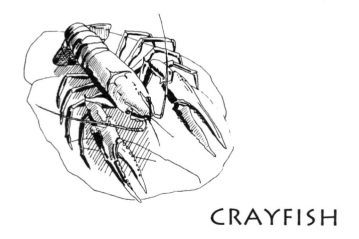

CRAYFISH

<u>Your starters:</u>

AY

way	kayak	relay	Golladay
bay	nosegay	Bombay	tray
tay	mayhem	spay	Wayne
cay	bayonet	clay	rayon
may	essay	haywire	cayenne
say	belaying pin	wayward	Maya
day	Bayonne	Mandalay	jaywalk
ray	Daytona Beach	Paraguay	Uruguay
gay	Dayton	Kaye	Skagway
lay	mayonnaise	Malaysia	Sayres
pay	crayfish	Payne	Hayden
hay	Hayward	Gaylord	Findlay
kay	Claybourne	Conway	Barclay
uay	Lindsay	Kayla	Jayne
fay	Fayettesville	Grayson	Taylor
	Galloway	Swayze	Albany
	Murray	Garroway	Lindsay
	Mayflower	layette	Caymans
	Blue Jays	bayberry	fayalite
	praying mantis	bayou	Maynard
	Day-Lewis	Thayer	Hayes
	grayling	Mayer	crayon
	Cayuga Lake	Tay-Sachs	Raymond

<u>Starters:</u>
Create a story about a sailing vacation you took.
Discuss a cajun cookin' show.

✍ **Your additions/notes**

gecKo

Your starters:

GE

geo	Gettysburg	bogey	tragedy
gef	gelding	Aegean	geisha
gec	Raggedy Ann	ageism	Gezira
get	Gemini	geyser	gecko
gez	gefilte fish	Genoa	Gestapo
gee	Geiger counter	geranium	forgery
gea	bungee	George	germ
gen	Bridgeman	gesso	Gerald
ges	Geronimo	Gephardt	gerbil
gel	gelatin	Geneva	progeny
ged	Gertrude	geneology	fogey
gem	Genghis Kahn	gender	Geissel
gey	gerontology	geometry	geology
ger	Gethsemene	Geraldine	ginger
gep	beget	gemstone	Genesis
gei	Geri	Gene	general
	Argentina	Agee	badger
	bourgeoisie	Bergen	Burgess

Starters:
Create a paragraph about great military strategists.
Create a television commercial for a pet store.

✍ **Your additions/notes**

HOwDy DooDy

<u>Your starters:</u>

OW

gow	Moscow	pillow	avow
vow	dowel	chowder	Kowloon
how	Howell	mown	Marlowe
row	widow	Powell	Solow
tow	Bowling Green	Bowe	Rowan
bow	cowberry	Howdy Doody	Bowen
jow	powder	Lowe	Iowa
low	endow	Howard	crown
mow	Townsend	vowel	kowtow
pow	cowl	howitzer	Knowles
cow	Georgetown	Howe	Downing
now	cowlick	dowdy	Gower
sow	crow	jowl	Howell
kow	bowel	chow	Cowper
dow	arrow	trowel	Downey
eow	Beowulf	Bowers	Rowena
iow	tallow	Kowalski	meow
	Garroway	sown	Turow
	McDowell	Glasgow	Farrow
	Janowitz	Lowry	Manilow
	Barrow	Calloway	Soweto
	Harlow	Browning	marrow
	Stowe	Woodrow	Cracow

Starters:
Discuss your vacation at a replica of a turn of the century village.
Describe the entertainment for New Year's Eve in Times Square.

✍ **Your   additions/notes**

lotus

<u>Your starters:</u>

OT

iot	Kotzebue	divot	Rotary
vot	robot	hotel	idiot
hot	potassium	totem	Visigoth
rot	Botswana	escargot	DeSoto
tot	Notre Dame	potpourri	motif
bot	Hottentot	botany	Scotland
sot	knot	Rothchild	moth
kot	Bardot	cotillion	Gotham
cot	pottery	votive	ascot
lot	lottery	Koto	sloth
pot	Timothy	Potter	rotunda
dot	Botticelli	mottled	antidote
got	cotangent	lotus	Motown
mot	Endicot	botulism	Epcot
oot	apothecary	notary	scooter
not	Potemkin	cotton	Mott
	Rotterdam	Potomac	ingot
	Amenhotep	Abbott	Alcott
	Aristotle	Blackfoot	Bogota
	root beer	Botha	boycott

Starters:
Create a short paragraph about the history of golf.
Create a short story about a food inspector.
Create a news release for the society column of the Atlanta Journal-Constitution.

✍ **Your   additions/notes**

Your starters:

AC

aac	Zodiac	extract	tacit
hac	Balzac	Stacy	miracle
mac	debacle	cache	shellac
zac	Jacques	sacrament	pinnacle
bac	vacancy	alpaca	shack
fac	Isaac	tobacco	tractor
lac	saccharine	interface	poach
oac	cactus	maniac	jackal
rac	dactylology	cognac	roach
tac	Sacramento	vacuum	taco
vac	hyacinth	exact	Rachel
iac	Peachtree	Bacchus	ipecac
cac	Appalachian	glacier	snack
sac	pachyderm	Grace	Tracy
wac	evacuate	Horace	Wallace
xac	pterodactyl	Candace	shackle
nac	papier mache	lactate	pact
jac	Hackensack	bacteria	Keach
eac	Adirondacks	Waco	Apache
yac	macaw	Bach	sumac
pac	Balzac	Blackfoot	facet
dac	Ohrbach	Jackson	Wallach
	Bacharach	Spacek	Liberace
	Caracas	Pensacola	Jack

Starters:
Explain how animal and plant life benefit the human condition.
Describe the worst motel experience you've had.
Describe how 'manifest destiny' impacted the indigenous peoples of North America.

✍ **Your   additions/notes**

TOUCAN

Your starters:

AN

man	swan	evangelist	Brian
ban	Mandy	Roanoke	toboggan
zan	Landry	Bunyan	Juan
can	Scranton	nanny	cancer
nan	Yankees	Bhutan	tank
wan	Mandarin	Byzantine	rancid
dan	Harlan	vandal	turban
oan	Tarzan	Jordan	Albania
van	Jane	iguana	Durante
ean	Portland	toucan	Bataan
pan	Xanadu	Vanderbilt	fangs
uan	Hank	Bridgeman	Ketchikan
fan	Trojan	oregano	Greenland
ran	Azerbaijan	Canberra	Panara
tan	Buchanan	Fant	Aristophanes
gan	Grant	Baranov	Randy
san	Afghanistan	Nancy	Yucatan
han	Balkan	Bancroft	Bangkok
kan	Bangladesh	Kannapell	gander
ian	wand	botany	Botswana
lan	Bozeman	Brando	Shanny
jan	Afrikaans	wean	Streisand
aan	Eleanor	Perlman	Danson
yan	Stanwyck	Alexander	Havilland
xan	Amanda	Travanti	Sutherland
	Rowan	Chang	Sullivan
	Fairbanks	Swanson	Caan
	Burbank	Constance	brandy
	Evans	Atlanta	Yucatan
	Bryant	Hyannis	Orlando
	panda	chant	Cuban
	Blanchard	Dean	bland

Starters:
Create a plot for a jungle movie.
Create a tall tale.

✍ **Your   additions/notes**

Your starters:

BU

bul	Bundy	bungee	Wilbur
buc	buzz	album	bully
buy	buckle	buxom	halibut
bub	Bullard	Kotzebue	robust
bus	Dubuque	Marbury	bugle
bug	buffer	Bubonic Plague	auburn
bue	Shrewsbury	Williamsburg	Buckingham
bun	Budapest	Buddha	Buster
but	buffalo	Augsburg	Bulgaria
buz	Hepburn	Bunyan	Burbank
buq	Burgess	Melbourne	Burr
bud	Istanbul	bursitis	Burundi
bum	Butler	buzzard	Gatlinburg
bux	rebus	rosebud	Burma
buf	Sears-Roebuck	Butte	Kennebunkporte
bur	Pittsburgh	Columbus	Istanbul
	Buchanan	Fredericksburg	Buena Vista
	Bucharest	Canterbury	Kanchanaburi
	bulb	Burt	Nebuchadnezzar
	Bradbury	Steenburgen	Lansbury
	Bunche	Arbus	Johannesburg
	Vicksburg	Kabul	Cadbury
	Burroughs	Harrisburg	Edinburgh

Starters:
Invent a science fiction story about alien plant forms.
Share your "around the world in eighty days" experience.

✍ **Your additions/notes**

Your starters:

L I

lix	Belize	helix	incline
lia	flirt	Phyllis	Frelich
lip	collie	alias	lidocaine
lij	lichen	lieutenant	lima bean
liz	lilac	Acropolis	Cornelius
lib	Madeline	Hlibok	Lipton
lin	liquor	blimp	liege
lif	Alice	scallion	sliver
lim	lizard	Libby	libel
lig	Liberia	Lisbon	Libertarian
lid	Clifton	Liechtenstein	lighthouse
lit	dahlia	Lima	limestone
liv	Lindbergh	Linton	Liszt
lio	Livingstone	adrenaline	alliteration
liq	Rosalie	Rhulin	ballistics
lie	Basilica	lingerie	blitzkrieg
liu	botulism	Liliuokalani	Natalie
lir	Somalia	Halifax	Medellin
lic	Melissa	Bolivia	Wheeling
lil	Williamsburg	Mahalia	Jacqueline
lis	Billings	Chillicothe	Malibu
	ligament	Elizabeth	Salinas
	Philippines	licorice	Eliot
	Limbaugh	Wellington	Montpellier
	relic	bliss	Carlisle
	Westphalia	Austerlitz	Allison
	Wylie	Sullivan	Phillip
	liver	Millicent	Maximillion
	Elijah	Franklin	Julie
	Lillian	linoleum	William
	Eliza	slicker	Billie

Starters:
Describe a pioneer diet.
Discuss the development of great societies in world history.

✍ **Your   additions/notes**

MOTH

Your starters:

-TH

ath	Elizabeth	Yarmouth	tenth
wth	wrath	Beth	Plymouth
nth	Duluth	Leavenworth	Bosworth
hth	myth	Portsmouth	Booth
uth	aftermath	width	Jareth
eth	cloth	Ithica	breath
dth	eighth	depth	Macbeth
xth	Ruth	growth	Fort Worth
yth	Dartmouth	Smith	filth
lth	mammoth	Monmouth	psychopath
oth	sixth	mirth	broth
fth	Roth	Sabbath	seventh
ith	Visigoth	Lillith	length
rth	monolith	bismuth	empath
gth	moth	hearth	wreath
pth	Seth	stealth	Forsooth!
	fifth	Edith	Garth
	Meredith	sheath	Perth

Starters:
Discuss the exploration and development of the East Coast of America.
Give the results of the Kentucky Derby.

✍ **Your   additions/notes**

QUILL

<u>Your   starters:</u>

QU

que	Quasimodo	acquittal	quiche
qui	quaint	Quebec	inquest
qua	squat	quessidilla	quotient
quo	lacquer	tequila	quartz
quy	squid	equator	quorum
	squeal	squawk	aqua
	quill	squirt	Jacques
	Quincy	queasy	quixotic
	exquisite	quarantine	Quaker
	quart	Mozambique	squad
	quilt	Queeg	Squanto
	squeamish	requisition	inquisition
	squash	aquarium	aqualung
	prerequisite	quota	equestrian
	Albuquerque	Quentin	squander
	Jacqueline	Marquette	Rehnquist
	Nyquil	baroque	quail
	burlesque	Chatauqua	Quayle
	Queens	mosque	Banquo
	applique	Quinn	conquistador
	Quetzalcoatl	soliloquy	Truth or Consequences
	arabesque	marquis	Jacques
	Don Quixote	de Becque	turquoise

Starters:

Tell of your experiences in a time-share condo in Acapulco.

Create a short mystery story.

Describe your search for salt water fish to display.

✍ **Your   additions/notes**

Your starters:

DI

dia	dizzy	dill	San Diego
diz	diamond	dipper	dimmer
dic	Benedict	Addis Ababa	diaper
dix	dice	Nadine	Madison
did	dive	dinette	armadillo
div	katydid	dial	Veditz
dik	dividend	podium	Dixon
die	Dixie	Dion	dictate
dij	endive	editor	dictator
dit	divert	diameter	Mogadishu
dig	soldier	division	Dirk
dis	Edith	digit	cardiogram
dil	Adirondacks	Dimitrov	edict
dir	Dijon	disco	director
dim	diva	Dick	Dioxin
dip	undies	audiogram	diet
din	Diana	Dinah	Dionne
dio	Mediterranean	digitalis	Vladimir
diu	Houdini	Disney	Diaz
	Meredith	DiMaggio	Judith
	valedictorian	Thorndike	Dillon
	Humperdink	Addison	Rushdie
	dialysis	Dickens	Obediah
	Arcadia	Fielding	Diane
	Madison	Kurdistan	Geraldine
	Sadie	Mandino	Carradine

Starters:
Create an exotic recipe.
Tell of a friend's experience in the emergency room.
Discuss Desert Storm.

✍ **Your   additions/notes**

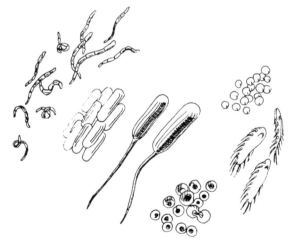

gErms & BacTerIa

Your starters:

ER

aer	Ulster	German	Aberdeen
der	Tucker	Adler	Kimberly
ger	opera	rudder	jerky
jer	juggler	Carver	herpes
mer	Esther	fern	germ
per	Frishberg	Lancaster	Gertrude
ter	foyer	thermal	leery
wer	Denver	blinker	Lauren
ser	Anderson	Cher	Montpelier
ner	kernel	glimmer	terminal
ker	cheer	Yerker	Bernadette
her	berth	Casper	pewter
eer	swerve	ambergris	Frederick
ber	insert	St. Petersburg	bacteria
ier	mermaid	versatile	Jeremiah
ver	sewer	whimper	Azerbaijan
ler	mixer	Vernon	Baedeker
xer	geranium	discern	Derrick
fer	aerospace	Mervin	steer
yer	boxer	Beecher	arteriosclerosis
cer	jerk	Western	bladder
zer	Ferrigno	gender	Jerry
	eerie	Pierre	nerd
	jeer	Walter	joker
	Cicero	Nigeria	Vera
	Homer	Cameroon	Sierra Leone
	Jasper	Beersheba	Albuquerque
	Teheran	Monterey	Chaucer
	gerund	Zinser	adder
	Heather	Sanderson	verse

Starters:
Tell a tale of early New England sea-goers.
Be an announcer for a body-building contest.

✍ **Your   additions/notes**

ArMADiLLO

Your starters:

M A

mac	Amazon	maximum	mannequin
maj	maple	Omaha	malt
map	mammal	dismay	Eastman
max	mare	Bismark	Maughn
mad	Guatemala	maze	macaroni
mam	Newman	Amarillo	Main
mat	hematoma	mackintosh	market
may	Widmark	mayor	Oman
mah	Mali	antimatter	Hoffman
man	mauve	Kalamazoo	cinematography
maz	Norman	armadillo	Somalia
mag	Dalmatian	mace	Mack
mau	maraschino	maize	Dumas
mal	Maui	maul	Chapman
mai	pyromania	nomad	sumac
mar	Marjory	magenta	Ishmael
mab	domain	damask	Matthew
mas	Thomas	majority	Appomatox
mae	Mark	Maghreb	DuMaurier
	LeMans	Rodman	Damascus
	Islamabad	Majorca	Kathmandu
	Boardman	Mason	Mathilda

Starters:
Describe the filming of an adventure movie in South America.
Create a travel commercial for the Southwest.

✍ **Your   additions/notes**

<u>Your starters:</u>

NG

ang	Bengal	pingpong	Cummings
ong	Santa Domingo	Lansing	angle
eng	Ingalls	Congo	Hemingway
ung	ganglia	belong	ranger
ing	dipthong	King Kong	strange
	Dangerfield	languish	jungle
	Birmingham	Browning	Englebert
	plunge	Shanghai	Palm Springs
	mongrel	Erting	mange
	engulf	Hong Kong	lung
	thong	Beijing	Angelou
	sting	gingivitis	Dominguez
	Wang	fungus	gong
	anguish	manger	sling
	Youngstown	meninges	Lange
	Wheeling	Singapore	Cheng
	Angola	Bangor	tango
	Springsteen	Chung	Lexington
	Ewing	kangaroo	Springfield
	hanger	Ming	Angela
	Jennings	endangered	Tangier
	Bing	sarong	Bangkok
	angina	Bangladesh	Irving
	ginger	Langella	Svengali
	angst	Benning	Ellington

Starters:
Describe getting to the Great Wall of China.
Discuss medical maladies of dogs.

✍ **Your   additions/notes**

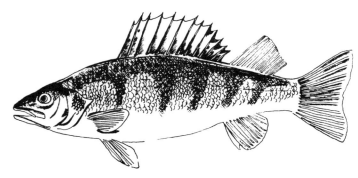

PERCH

Your starters:

CH

cha	Richter	chrome	Achilles
che	perch	chimpanzee	choreograph
chi	franchise	Natchitoches	Chris
cho	Apache	echo	chimney
chr	Charles	Weitbrecht	chess
chu	alchemy	hypochondriac	Archimedes
chl	chowder	chlorine	Chester
rch	mulch	Sanchez	cholera
ach	chancre	nachos	Buchanan
lch	Schultz	avalanche	chlorophyll
ech	chili	Kamchatka	ochre
nch	woodchuck	Parcheesi	chrysanthemum
ich	artichoke	chalk	poncho
tch	Cher	schooner	Nietzsche
och	Chile	Ichabod	Szechuan
sch	Scholls	brunch	Long Beach
uch	cochlea	orchid	champagne
	Gilchrist	chokeberry	Bucharest
	gulch	Czechoslovakia	birch
	Fleischman	mulch	Winchester
	crochet	beech	Reich
	Wichita	Benchley	Cochran
	Crichton	Jericho	archery
	Fletcher	Wallach	Saskatchewan
	Chet	Chillicothe	Richard
	Munich	Chaney	Beecher
	Churchill	Petruchio	Prairie du Chien
	Michael	Natchez	Chung
	Cratchit	Chad	Nichols
	Schaeffer	Dietrich	Chernobyl

Starters:
Create a press release for the first day of the Olympics.
Describe the local flora and fauna.

✍ **Your   additions/notes**

Your starters:

ST

str	mastadon	Webster	Steiger
yst	angst	Dustin	Amsterdam
stl	hostage	Castro	fistula
est	styrofoam	ostrich	Christopher
sto	asthma	heist	Charleston
ust	St. Ives	destiny	Mostel
bst	chestnut	Justin	VISTA
sti	rust	pistachio	gastritis
sto	Costa Rica	Khuzistan	cestode
mst	Ustinov	mystery	Rastafarian
gst	wisteria	Struthers	Flagstaff
ste	Stanley	homestead	osteopath
ast	zest	Houston	Astros
xst	Ernest	Stephanie	bustle
lst	estrogen	Pakistan	Kristofferson
nst	Astin	mustang	Stowe
stu	crustacean	Nostradamus	distill
ist	Stockholm	mustard	Pabst
sta	strait	jester	Listerine
rst	Ulster	isthmus	Woodstock
sty	gusto	Pasteur	Steelers
	Jamestown	histamine	Sault Ste. Marie
	Stewart	asterisk	Dostoevsky
	Key West	pastry	vestibule
	nasturtium	Asti Spumante	Estella
	gristle	Istanbul	Styron
	hysteria	Kingston	Heston
	yeast	Costello	Falstaff
	Leichtenstein	astigmatism	Steve
	cystic fibrosis	Straub	Estrada

Starters:
Discuss the benefits of having all-sports channels.
Describe some home remedies for common ailments.

✍ **Your   additions/notes**

Your starters:

OU

dou	Houdini	Vancouver	pouch
gou	Wouk	poultry	Houston
eou	bourbon	clout	toucan
tou	Plymouth	Angelou	profound
you	O'Rourke	bouquet	trout
bou	voucher	journal	Douglas
hou	couscous	devour	mousse
pou	Courtney	dough	fountain
vou	Louis	journey	compound
cou	gourd	gourmet	Sioux City
jou	Proust	Louisville	devout
rou	wound	Youngstown	Soukup
wou	scout	Louise	Goulet
fou	foul	gout	Theroux
lou	joust	Melbourne	Dartmouth
iou	goulash	Calhoun	Boulder
mou	Scarborough	bout	gouge
	Toulouse	Seoul	couplet
	Houseman	Lourdes	Gould
	Newfoundland	Kerouac	Council Bluffs
	Houston	Lamour	Gloucester

Starters:
Describe a pilgrimage to Mecca.
Create a Shakespearean poem.

✍ **Your   additions/notes**

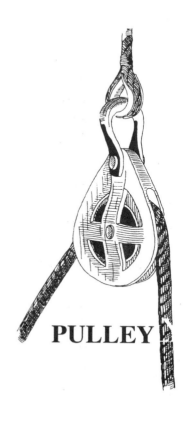

PULLEY

Your starters:

LE

lev	athlete	Adler	Leigh
lem	Yuletide	leprosy	levy
leh	leukemia	Charles	leek
lea	celebrity	lemmings	New Orleans
led	lexicon	legend	league
les	Bellefonte	reflex	pulley
ley	leotard	leech	parallel
lei	Achilles	Gallileo	Raleigh
lec	lease	cleft	juggler
leo	burlesque	leviathan	lever
lew	Alec	Lebanon	Marlee
lef	lentil	Allegheny	sleigh
len	Cleveland	leprechaun	sleazy
let	leopard	Harlem	leather
leb	Leningrad	cleats	Lexington
lel	lesion	Clemson	Lehmann
ler	Gleason	leash	Cleopatra
leu	Hamlet	Keller	Aleutian Islands
lee	barley	Berkley	arteriosclerosis
lep	Salem	Miller	petroleum
lex	elephantiasis	scarlet fever	Fuller
leg	Letterman	Lewis	Pledge
	Fowler	Charleston	Tyler

Starters:
Describe early medical techniques.
Create a diary entry for William Clark, on his expedition to find the Northwest Passage.

✍ **Your   additions/notes**

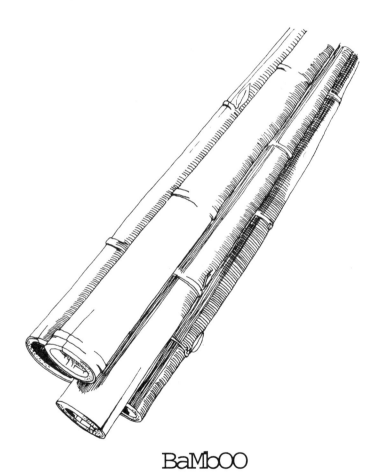

BaMbOO

<u>Your starters:</u>

BA

bab	baptism	Bahamas	cabbage
baf	Albany	cabana	Birnbaum
bas	Baxter	tubas	bailiff
bav	baobab	Baja	Sinbad
bak	Baal	wombat	Bahrain
bae	Alabama	baleen	bazaar
baw	baklava	Bauer	rutabaga
bar	bayou	babushka	Bambi
bam	Bavaria	bawdy	embalm
bad	Cuban	embargo	Battle Creek
bal	Bayonne	Cobain	badger
bay	bayonet	Bataan	turban
bao	bamboo	Baedeker	bait
bac	baffle	ambassador	Bombay
baz	Sabatini	Baum	combat
baa	Barbara	Bangor	imbalance
bap	bagpipe	batik	Baily
ban	Mombasa	Fairbanks	Sebastian
bai	bagel	Baldwin	Baton Rouge
bax	Shabazz	baccalaureate	bas mitzvah
bah	Bahan	ballad	basilica
bau	bacteria	Bahai	embassy
bag	Bali	Raban	bassoon
baj	Hobart	Basil	Burban
bat	Baghdad	Banff	Zimbalist
	Obadiah	Wambaugh	Balzac
	bazooka	Baker	Zimbabwe
	Rosenbaum	Bagnkok	Lombardi
	Brisbane	Robards	Hannibal

Starters:
Describe your experience at Woodstock II.
Describe a Congressional fact-finding mission to Africa.

✍ **Your   additions/notes**

beluga

Your starters:

BE

bet	libel	Benjamin	beatnik
bei	belch	beri-beri	bezel
bey	ibex	robber	Belfast
bed	beehive	Rebecca	beaver
beg	Beulah	obey	beryl
beu	beige	Bellugi	Frisbee
bel	Caribbean	Betsy	beware
bec	behemoth	Berber	Bessie
beq	sherbet	bevy	befuddled
beh	Bedouin	beluga	globes
bee	abbey	Bert	beta
bez	Beatrice	Albee	unbeknownst
bea	Belgium	Reuben	begonia
ben	benign	robed	Becky
bev	Tibet	sorbet	Beverly
bes	Bedrock	Belize	bemoan
bef	bequest	slobber	Beth
bex	bevel	Belinda	Berlin
ber	benzene	Belle	grabbed
bek	Benin	bellow	Bengal
bem	iceberg	Benson	beech
bew	Thebes	Gilbert	Brubeck
	Ellerbee	Canberra	Uzbekistan
	Beiderbecke	Quebec	Oberammergau
	Elizabeth	embedded	Eikenberry
	Bombeck	Gobel	Rodenberry
	Greenberg	Chamberlain	raspberry
	Liberia	Speilberg	Rebecca
	Bel Geddes	Robert	Lindbergh

Starters:
Discuss the plots of the Star Trek Movies.
Describe a mining operation.

✍ **Your   additions/notes**

fly fishing

Your   starters:

I S

lis	epistle	Curtis	Fiske
uis	paisley	wisteria	cloister
bis	histamine	Disney	biscuit
wis	Kissinger	oasis	Louis
nis	existentialism	Dukakis	chemist
gis	axis	commissioner	fistula
dis	Bristol	Memphis	Clarissa
ais	daisy	mistletoe	Dennis
ris	prism	Tunis	porpoise
yis	Eisenhower	vivisection	obelisk
ois	Lewis	pistachio	Clovis
fis	Pisces	catharsis	Paris
cis	oralism	caddis	Gengis Khan
sis	eidelweiss	lobbyist	Weiss
vis	Francis	piscatology	Harrisburg
xis	amaryllis	Regis	dispensary
his	Taoist	psoriasis	kismet
eis	Lisa	fissure	Kurdish
kis	geisha	shish kabob	disco
mis	Chris	Phyllis	Sunkist
pis	thistle	Fischer	sistrum
	Nissan	Morris	cistern
	taxis	Boise	debris
	bassoonist	Denise	feisty
	Bismarck	Kaiser	bliss
	Sisyphus	risotto	Pisa
	arsonist	epidermis	Liszt
	Chisolm	nudist	bison
	Vishnu	squeamish	Melissa
	Guisewite	Annapolis	Giselle

Starters:
Tell a little about how to get started in fly-fishing.
Create a story for an animated movie.

✍ **Your   additions/notes**

<u>Your   starters:</u>

TO

tov	topiary	hoity-toity	October
tor	toucan	Toyota	toffee
tom	Todd	stove	Barstow
top	toxic	totem	Tokyo
toa	toggle	Stokoe	Toby
toz	Tocqueville	tostada	lactose
tot	inventory	Torquemada	cartoon
toi	Baton Rouge	piston	plutocracy
tob	tortilla	Charleton	Toussaint L'Overture
toq	festoon	tower	Tobiah
tow	toddler	Topeka	toque
tog	Toledo	Johnston	stomach
toc	equator	Stowe	Bloomington
toy	Victoria	stoma	intoxicant
tou	burritos	Hamilton	Toulouse-Latrec
tod	aristocracy	Whitestone	diastole
tok	toupee	Houston	toiletry
ton	tole	Toffler	toga
tof	token	dermatologist	Tommy
tox	Toscanini	topaz	Toronto
tos	Townsend	Tolkein	mastectomy
too	Estonia	stork	Motown
tol	mycetozan	Tolstoy	Torah
	potatoes	Togo	toboggan
	tourniquet	Saskatoon	atom

Starters:
Describe the food in a Tex-Mex restaurant.
Discuss specializations in medicine.

✍ **Your   additions/notes**

Your starters:

DE

dea	codeine	Tilden	Deborah
der	adequate	mildew	Rolodex
dex	Degas	adenoid	deuce
deo	derrick	Delhi	Arden
deh	ambidextrous	epidermis	derby
dec	denim	deja vu	DeKalb
dee	dehumidifier	Odets	Andes
del	Redden	citadel	Liddell
deu	Death Valley	defibrillate	Judea
des	Deuteronomy	de Gaulle	Des Moines
den	Adele	ordeal	Odessa
ded	Dewey	dextrose	Dennis
deg	dandelion	deduction	decaffeinated
dem	deacon	indecent	Gideon
dew	cadet	Dexter	depilatory
dep	Deidre	pandemonium	deBergerac
dei	delicatessen	Decatur	Cinderella
def	Devereux	cadence	rodeo
dek	Padden	Defoe	Hindenberg
deq	Debussy	Endeavor	DeeDee
dej	deoxidize	Denver	Dexedrine
deb	Dewars	Fidel	Demi
det	Mandela	Amadeus	Zydeko
dev	Anderson	Denny	Trudeau
	Euripedes	Pirandello	Deighton
	Pasedena	Delphi	Valdez
	Mordecai	Thaddeus	Providence
	vaudeville	Bel Geddes	Alexander
	Delany	Flanders	Bordeaux
	Depp	dehydration	Hades

Starters:
Describe your high school reunion.
Explain the rise of the entertainment industry in America since the 1900's.

✍ **Your   additions/notes**

REINDEER

<u>Your starters:</u>

IN

min	Lincoln	bingo	Patinkin
fin	marina	raisin	Melvin
vin	penicillin	Cincinnati	assassin
tin	linguist	penguin	kinescope
ain	Einstein	hyacinth	dinosaur
hin	Bravin	sirloin	Coughlin
sin	pinata	Quincy	vintage
zin	reindeer	sprain	Dinah
din	albino	Finland	ginger
iin	Racine	Singleton	Rin Tin Tin
oin	skiing	morphine	gingivitus
kin	gingham	Nintendo	finch
bin	Erin	binary	Schein
gin	mint	linen	Singapore
pin	cinnamon	Virginia	Hindu
win	cinquain	twine	thorazine
rin	Maine	ginseng	Linda
uin	binomial	Cinderella	cinema
cin	groin	aspirin	Minnesota
ein	lingerie	quintuplets	veterinarian
nin	Mt. McKinley	instinct	ninny
lin	shingle	Twin Falls	kinetics
jin	Elgin	rosin	Catherine
	winery	vinegar	scintillate
	mink	Clinton	dingo
	jinx	tinsel	aborigine

Starters:
Create a new, spectacular jump for Evel Knievel.
Describe your stay at a winter resort.

✍ **Your   additions/notes**

Your starters:

EN

gen	incense	Benjamin	Tolkien
wen	Owen	ventriloquist	Lorenzo
ken	xenophobia	menu	Glenn
hen	dendrite	penguin	mentor
cen	Tennyson	Renoir	venison
ven	Cenozoic	adenoids	oxygen
fen	baleen	Allen	Rosen
jen	Olsen	venereal	Genghis Khan
ten	centaur	pendulum	Jennifer
yen	kennel	Zenith	Mendelssohn
den	Wenceslaus	meningitis	fennel
ien	centrifugal	Vienna	Sonnenstrahl
ren	renaissance	genealogy	Venezuela
xen	Queens	Rickenbacker	Hawken
een	Pendelton	Aspen	detergent
pen	adreneline	Vincent	amniocentisis
zen	centipede	Irene	Gwendolyn
men	Xenos	Armenia	Kenya
ben	Lentz	Pensacola	Reno
len	yenta	penicillin	Polident
sen	Mendoza	Quentin	tentacle
nen	venom	Kennedy	Athens
	Chen	Ellen	MacKenzie
	Reuben	Sentra	hallucinagen
	cayenne	blender	Ogden
	Laurent	Bienvenu	Eugene
	Spencer	Trenton	detergent
	extensor	Charlene	Leavenworth
	Benghazi	Yemen	Campho-Phenique
	Bowling Green	Phoenix	Cheyenne

Starters:
Describe a meeting of UN delegates.
Create a story about a great paleontologist's discoveries.

✍ **Your   additions/notes**

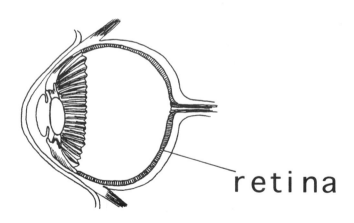

retina

<u>Your starters:</u>

RE

rel	paregoric	Dreyfus	Schreiber
rey	toreador	reindeer	Brenda
ref	Freda	streusel	werewolf
rej	Brezhnev	Crete	Fremont
rea	trek	Jared	horehound
rer	areola	morel	Irene
rez	Theresa	urethra	crewel
rev	crematorium	Karen	Meredith
ret	Precambrian	credenza	Freud
rei	pretzel	presbycusis	gremlin
reo	Humphrey	oregano	Breathalyzer
res	grebe	Greenwich	trefoil
rew	Hereford	prejudice	creosote
reh	streptococcus	Reuben	Frey
reb	Laredo	Jeremy	serendipity
ree	brewery	Fresno	crepe
rek	Dreiser	prehensile	Brecht
reu	Treblinka	retina	relish
req	fresco	Ares	creel
rec	Lorenzo	norepinephrine	Gretchen
rem	Drew	prey	Terezina
red	breviary	Oregon	Brewster
rep	Moreau	requiem	Grenoble
reg	Lorelei	rebus	Regis
ren	Reich	wren	rerun
	Alvarez	Buenos Aires	Reynolds
	puree	trellis	Korea

Starters:
Describe daily life on an 19th century farm.
Create a high school history book entry about World War II.

✍ **Your additions/notes**

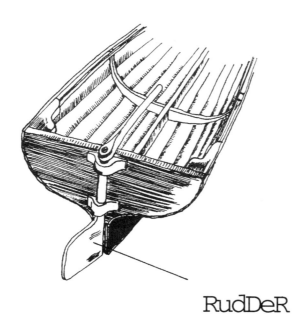

RudDeR

<u>Your starters:</u>

RU

r u t	truffle	Aruba	crustacean
r u k	Ruth	bruise	Trudy
r u f	grub	Druid	chorus
r u b	crux	fructose	Faruk
r u r	Trudeau	quorum	Brussels
r u l	virus	Peruvian	brusque
r u z	thesaurus	cruise	truant
r u s	corrugated	Trujillo	gruel
r u h	Rubicon	Caruso	Prudence
r u a	Horus	Drury Lane	Veracruz
r u e	crucifix	rubella	krugeraand
r u m	rumba	cruller	gerund
r u p	Rutledge	strudel	crudites
r u n	cruet	Uruguay	rugby
r u x	serum	thrush	Rumania
r u c	Ruhr	brucellosis	Jerusalem
r u g	prune	forum	syrup
r u i	rutabaga	Truman	Truk Islands
r u v	Rudolph	Russell	Rushmore
r u j	Burundi	rudder	grunion
r u d	rupee	grunt	Prudhoe Bay
	Brutus	spruce	Rumplestiltskin
	Trump	Rubaiyat	New Brunswick
	Bruce	caruncle	ruminant
	ruble	Grundy	Struthers
	Prussia	Beirut	Rutherford
	Crusoe	Rufus	gurus

Starters:
Discuss the exchange rate among international currencies.
Tell of your experience on the Deaf Cruise.

✍️ **Your   additions/notes**

GIANT PANDA BEAR

<u>Your starters:</u>

P A

pak	pagan	Nepal	pancreas
pab	Pakistan	pabulum	Paul
pav	topaz	paella	opal
pal	Pacific	Parsons	paisley
pac	pavillion	parka	pajamas
paz	pachyderm	pageant	Tai-pan
pag	spawn	Zapata	parfait
pas	padlock	Panara	Dogpatch
paw	palette	patent	parable
pad	pauper	parrot	La Paz
paj	Paris	Kampala	Parker
pap	Sao Paulo	Patinkin	Pasternak
pae	Palmyra	Appalachia	Pago Pago
pau	Pasadena	El Paso	Paraguay
pai	Papas	Fittipaldi	Tampax
pan	sampan	tarpaulin	Paiute
pat	Paganini	papaya	Paddington
par	pampas	Palaeolithic	Pawtucket
pah	Patrick	sarsparillla	capacitor
	parakeet	Panama	Painesville
	Patrie	leopard	empanada
	pagoda	chaparral	pantry
	Pascal	Rampart	Pahlavi
	Packers	pasta	Giant Panda Bear

Starters:
Describe the victory lap at a NASCAR race.
Tell about your day at the zoo.

✍ **Your   additions/notes**

Your starters:

EM

lem	pemmican	Hemingway	cement
yem	remedy	Demerol	per diem
cem	Schemenauer	femur	seminary
tem	blemish	hematoma	membrane
dem	Rembrandt	Agamemnon	Bethlehem
sem	Harlem	Bremen	Templeton
eem	Klemperer	Dempsey	memorial
rem	Gleem	Jemimah	hemorrhoid
fem	lemming	Shemp	Desdemona
pem	tempo	Demetria	hemlock
gem	Memphis	Seminole	alchemy
oem	Bohemia	Salem	dementia
hem	Hemsley	The Supremes	Yemen
mem	Lemmon	semantics	stem
iem	goyem	nemesis	DeMille
nem	poem	hemophilia	Gemini
jem	lemur	Remington	tempera
	anemone	Guatemala	Jerusalem
	elementary	nemesis	The Temptations
	hemp	tempura	democracy

Starters:
Describe your musical odyssey from Motown to Graceland.
Discuss great literature through the ages.

✍ **Your   additions/notes**

<u>Your starters:</u>

TE

t e r	platelets	Whitehorse	Stewart
t e g	Tennyson	teflon	Hammerstein
t e w	betel nut	Entebbe	Burnstein
t e c	Chester	amniocentesis	Laertes
t e o	Gazeteer	Waterstreet	Pasternak
t e x	artery	Aztec	Steppenwolf
t e m	catechism	hostel	tequilla
t e a	Sternberg	Terre Haute	Costello
t e f	teak	Tennille	goiter
t e p	Austen	Tehran	protein
t e v	Bates	tether	Steve
t e b	arteriosclerosis	Van Patten	Ortega
t e n	intern	telekinesis	Steiger
t e t	Tel Aviv	Linkletter	Witter
t e h	Guatemala	Amenhotep	bacteria
t e i	Fayetteville	context	Potemkin
t e q	mastectomy	Steinbeck	Stephen
t e e	Amsterdam	ureter	totem
t e l	Terry	Mostel	osteoblasts
t e s	Lancaster	latex	tarantella
	protege	Rubenstein	Peter
	Baxter	stew	tempura
	meteor	techno-babble	register

Starters:
Create a Gilligan's Island episode.
Discuss modern day breakthroughs which make life easier.

IX

pix	pixie	vixen	mixture
dix	Phoenix	fixture	Dixie
fix	Dixon	Nixon	dominatrix
bix	suffix	Bixby	Bendix
mix	Hendrix	cervix	appendix
vix			
nix			
rix			

OX

dox	Lennox	Orthodox	foxtail
nox	proximity	phlox	paradox
tox	Biloxi	Hydrox	boxer
lox	Appomatox	amoxycilin	peroxide
mox	toxin	doxology	intoxicant
box	Madox	Xerox	Knoxville
rox			
fox			

AX

tax	Halifax	taxi	laxative
sax	Ajax	saxophone	anthrax
rax	ataxia	Paxton	taxidermy
jax	Baxter	Maxine	Pollifax
max	Maxwell	syntax	thorax
lax			
bax			
pax			
fax			

EX

lex	Essex	ibex	Plexiglass
tex	Chex	Rexall	ambidextrous
bex	cortex	reflex	hexagon
dex	Sussex	Kleenex	textile
hex	Lexington	Alexander	solar plexus
nex	annex	Middlesex	Rolex
sex			
rex			

UX

tux	tuxedo	Bordeaux	buxom
bux	juxtapose	Luxor	Huxley
hux	Maddux	Deveraux	Leroux
aux	Luxembourg	auxillary	Huxtable
jux	reflux	Sioux	
lux			
dux			
oux			

NX

inx	jinx	lynx	Bronx
onx	larynx		
ynx			

Starters:
Discuss life in New York City at the turn of the 20th century.
Describe your tour of great mansions of the South.

DOUBLE LETTERS

Reminder: For double letters, different methods including the slide (d→d), the bounce (d⌒d), and the tap (d⌄d) are all used. Find which is the most comfortable and efficient for you.

Schaffer	scaffold	Supalla	safflower
Annapolis	sapphire	Minneapolis	essay
cayenne	Allegheny	Fudd	Sonnenstrahl
Ferrigno	Pippen	Appomatox	guillotine
Raggedy Ann	Gettysburg	Burgess	Abbe de l'Epee
Alcott	Cogswell	potassium	potpourri
Powell	Valli	Padden	Bragg
vacuum	saccharine	haddock	armadillo
Sullivan	cabbage	mammary	jamboree
Afrikaans	Covell	Botticelli	Shelley
Kennebunkport	buzzard	pemmican	hemorrhoid
Massieu	Bataan	ballistics	scallion
mannequin	Matthew	Parcheesi	Achilles
Marcella	Lennox	chlorophyll	Shiite
baleen	Glenn	whittle	Lennon
Blackfoot	penicillin	Jennifer	juggler
Bullard	Golladay	Jerry	Canberra
Louisville	Phyllis	O'Donnell	Redden
Graybill	puzzle	acquittal	broccoli
Aaron	Sally	Shanny	dill
gossamer	Tinkerbell	gunnysack	Nunn
fennel	Twiggy	Brigadoon	satellite
tattoo	sarsaparilla	Waterstreet	Saab
Keller	Medoff	bouillon	Gannon
Marlee	lemmings	Cincinnati	Lucille
Cinderella	ambassador	Rebecca	Caribbean
Bette	Tar Heel	amaryllis	Tommy
Saskatoon	Dennis	DeeDee	grizzly
briquette	ratatouille	graffiti	tyrannosaurus
Trujillo	Brussels	llama	mongoose
Jimmy	Connolly	Lynette	Kannapell
William	La Jolla	caffeine	Fullerton
Larry	truffle	Kendall	molasses
Bellugi	Garretson	Merrill	Ballentyne

✍ **Your   additions/notes**

Your starters:

3

4

0

7

8

9

2

1

6

5

NUMERIC

INFORMATION

2

9

6

8

3

7

5

0

1

4

Signing TIME

The sign TIME is often included in the message.
    Example:
        English: Class begins at 8:00.
        ASL: CLASS BEGIN TIME 8

A.M. and P.M. information is included before the numeric information.
    Example:
        CLASS BEGIN MORNING TIME 8
        CLASS BEGIN NIGHT TIME 8

Time is signed like a digital clock rather than an analog clock.
    Example:
        MY PLANE TAKE-OFF MORNING TIME 9-50
    not   My plane leaves at ten 'til ten.

When signing an "on the hour" (TIME 5, TIME 9) the hand makes a small shake back and forth. If the time includes hour plus minutes (5:15, 3:40, 9:24) the hand does not shake.

In informal conversation, the base hand for MINUTE can be converted to a passive index touching the bottom of the palm of the dominant hand.

Signing AGE

Age can be represented very formally or very informally.
>   Example:
>>   'My dad is 53 years old' can be signed:

>   Formal: MY FATHER HIMSELF 53 YEAR OLD
>   Less formal: MY FATHER HIMSELF OLD 53

>>   'My dad is in his 50's' can be signed:

>>   MY FATHER OLD 5 (shake)
>   or   MY FATHER 5 (index of the five touches chin,
>>   then moves out to shake)

Very informally, as in the last example, the base sign OLD can be dropped, and the number sign begins at the chin and sweeps out.
>   Example:
>>   'My niece is three years old' can be signed:

>>   MY NIECE 3 (index of the 'three' touches chin
>>   and the sweeps out. Do not shake.)

Signing TELEPHONE NUMBERS

There are two options employed when signing telephone numbers.
>   Example:
>>   545-8639 can be signed:

>>   5-4-5 pause 8-6-3-9

>   or   5-4-5 pause 86-39

When an area code is included, another pause is added.
>   Example:
>>   (907) 545-8639 can be signed:
>>   9-0-7 pause 5-4-5 pause 8-6-3-9

Telephone   Number   Practice

349-6023	345-0707	274-7296
561-2454	745-7715	376-4000
943-7255	864-1353	450-5060
495-6559	562-4913	277-0045
521-6325	220-1113	257-1722
338-1122	783-4338	454-9802
402-2969	714-2360	860-0378
522-4009	310-4067	522-5325
563-4418	561-2488	257-5220
349-9344	337-7316	272-9193
373-2199	739-1944	761-4511
277-7851	892-8714	753-1844
248-2445	345-9905	293-3014
868-8219	406-3826	929-1813
694-8040	333-6620	555-1212
264-0218	924-6899	276-8917
876-3872	802-3716	913-0028
309-2159	521-2860	756-4643

Signing MONEY

One through nine dollars can be signed by incorporating the number sign with a wrist turn/flip. The more formal number-plus-the-DOLLAR-sign may also be used.

     Example:

          BOOK "S-I-L-E-N-T D-A-N-C-E-S" IT COST 4~DOLLAR

   or

          BOOK "S-I-L-E-N-T D-A-N-C-E-S" IT COST 4 DOLLAR

Dollar amounts higher than nine must use the number-plus-the-DOLLAR-sign.

The sign CENT can be incorporated before or after the numeric information.

     Example:

          THERE STORE 7-11 POP COST CENT 75

      or   THERE STORE 7-11 POP COST 75 CENT

However, the signs for specific coins always incorporate the numeric sign AFTER the CENT sign.

     Example:

Penny	=	CENT ONE
Nickel	=	CENT FIVE
Dime	=	CENT TEN
QUARTER	=	CENT TWENTY-FIVE

When signing the price of something that includes both dollar and cent information, The signs DOLLAR and CENT can be incorporated, and/or the decimal point can be included by using the sign PERIOD.

     Example:

          PAST MONTH MY B-I-L-L ELECTRICITY
          26 DOLLAR 52 CENT

          PAST MONTH MY B-I-L-L ELECTRICITY
           DOLLAR 26 PERIOD 52

Money   Practice

$17.20	$18.08	$19.88
$6.51	$1,219.32	$4,554.99
$19.71	$0.68	$99,210.00
$31.14	$77.16	$0.46
$57,946.00	$27.05	$50.00
$89.95	$42.60	$291.79
$5.00	$6.45	$1.50
$0.12	$319.80	$311,829.00
$25,416.00	$8.00	$9,413.10
$7,518.00	$2.50	$4,031.00
$300.87	$15.49	$23.02
$1,489,311.67	$8.76	$168.99
$17.47	$45.56	$64.80
$12.60	$325.00	$9.85
$32.87	$99.19	$82.02
$132.18	$60.73	$269.81
$29.40	$14.75	$1,099.71
$48.31	$5,664.68	$37.45

Signing DATES

Years are signed as they are spoken.
Example:

1963 =	19-63	not	1-9-6-3
1512 =	15-12	not	1-5-1-2

Years ending in 00 (1700, 1800, etc.) can be signed two different
ways.
Example:

                17-00
or   17-C

There are two signing options when referring to decades (the 1830's,
the 1970's).
Example:

         18-30 plus s (wrist twist)
         19-<u>7</u> (shake the 7)

Longer month names tend to be abbreviated; shorter month names
are spelled in their entirety.
Example:

January/J-A-N	July/J-U-L-Y
February/F-E-B	August/A-U-G
March/M-A-R-C-H	September/S-E-P-T
April/A-P-R-I-L	October/O-C-T
May/M-A-Y	November/N-O-V
June/J-U-N-E	December/D-E-C

When signing a month, day and year, two options may be employed.
Example:

December 27, 1943 could be signed:

        D-E-C 27 (hold the "7" for a slight pause) 19-43
or   12 (pause, slight shift) 27 (pause, slight shift) 43*

        *This tends to be used especially when sharing
birthdates, so the "19"00 part is assumed.

Date and Year Practice

1980	1964	1978
September 15, 1985	1829	1510
1860's	1486	October 9, 1942
1967	February 12, 1798	1948
July 4, 1776	1901	1924
1963	June 14, 1959	1940's
1875	1922	April 15, 1947
December 21, 1950	1632	1526
1983	1933	1792
January 26, 1984	1992	1965
1408	1646	November 24
1961	March 19, 1932	1608
1713	1946	1444
May 26, 1893	1974	August 5, 1994
1044	1517	1978
1911	June 24, 1963	1812
1864	1921	1723
February 29, 1996	1873	July 14, 1784

Signing Addresses

Street addresses are signed as they are spoken.
    Example:
                1682 Oak Avenue can be signed:

                16-82 O-A-K   A-V-E
        or   1-6-8-2 O-A-K   A-V-E

                301 Hayford Lane would be signed:

                3-0-1 H-A-Y-F-O-R-D   L-N
        not   3-C-1 H-A-Y-F-O-R-D   L-N

                523 Washington Drive would be signed:

                5-2-3 W-A-S-H-I-N-G-T-O-N   D-R
        or   5-23 W-A-S-H-I-N-G-T-O-N   D-R

The signs NORTH, SOUTH, EAST, WEST are included if they are part of
the address.
    Example:
                301 W. Hayford Lane would be signed:

                3-0-1 WEST H-A-Y-F-O-R-D   L-N

Addresses with apartment numbers include the signed abbreviation
A-P-T.
    Example:
                846 S. Main St. #7 would be signed:

                8-4-6 SOUTH M-A-I-N- S-T   A-P-T   7

Zip codes are signed number by number.
    Example:
                95324 would be signed:

                9-5-3-2-4
        not   9-53-24

Address   Practice

800 E. Third Avenue	504 Laurel Boulevard
1200 K Street	509 W. Diamond Lane
3300 Chestnut Road	9440 Wyoming Drive
3501 Jefferson Street	4325 W. 5th Avenue
1500 N. Jackson Avenue	7001 Sycamore Parkway
3111 Post Road	3901 S. 4th Avenue
3546 LaSalle Boulevard	2709 Providence Drive
2476 E. Tudor Road	4201 S. Main Street
605 Maple Drive	2838 Porcupine Drive
47092 Gambell Way	6 Newton Street
10900 Washington Drive #4	2216 C Street
605 Raspberry Road	12701 Alpine Drive #5C
12123 Clark Avenue	5866 Adenmoor Drive
7695 9th Street	4936 North Ashgrove Lane
214 State Road #3B	7091 Lincoln Circle
9731 Walker Boulevard	6854 Beach Boulevard #114
5270 Cumberland Drive	7878 186th Avenue
26 Walnut Hill Drive	916 East Front Street

Number   Practice

348	623	858	587
157	381	793	925
491	137	459	281
835	957	325	535
947	473	935	225
693	846	279	423
298	592	168	571
167	158	723	392
724	923	624	341
169	425	359	723
248	561	851	153
825	223	268	125
375	749	323	174
725	682	492	237
836	541	270	804
126	460	123	512
1,232	506	318	1,700
991	477	2,514	911
3,316	1,122	6,050	421
232	9,367	4,506	970
2,112	5,911	2,207	167
7,510	3,123	640	8,015
5,917	227	48,711	399
81,259	3,817	9,876	25,505
2,615	77,422	13,627	63,336
11,321	62,397	42,280	777,777
17,725	29,320	3,635	23,924
635,983	392	2,012	306
590	4,901	97,013	10,689
8,026	316,929	407	525

Mixed Numeric Practice

495-6559	477	405 S. 36th Avenue
$19.71	562-4913	2,207
1983	318	$0.68
48932 Benson Boulevard	3,123	563-4418
421	257-5220	6,050
349-9344	1933	911
$6.51	1,232	$4,554.99
January 26, 1984	$27.05	26 E. Dowling Road
$99,210.00	232	April 15, 1947
1965	$31.14	5,911
3721 Boniface Parkway	1922	783-4338
$57,946.00	640	December 21, 1950
1875	561-2488	$50.00
1600 Pennsylvania Avenue	1632	3,316
1,700	337-7316	$77.16
12450 W. 289th Avenue	1992	3351 Arctic Way #8
277-0045	$0.46	9,367
6411 DeBarr Road #23 D	272-9193	10 Downing Street

Videotapes and Computer Software for Practice

Fingerspelling: Expressive and Receptive Fluency. Joyce Linden Groode. DawnSign Press,1992.

Fingerspelling Practice Tapes. Sign Media, Inc., 1991
    (Four tapes are available: Fingerspelling Proper Names, Fingerspelling Geographic Locations, Fingerspelling Miscellaneous Items, and Fingerspelled Loan Signs)

Fingerspelling and Numbers. Interactive Sign Language, 1992.
    (For both Microsoft Windows and Macintosh)
    Available through Sign Enhancers, Inc.

FINGERSPELLING THE REAL WORLD

A book for fingerspelling practice specifically designed for students!

Over 2,000 practice words

names from Deaf history and culture
names from popular culture
geographic locations
terminology from science and nature, history, industry, leisure

~PLUS~

- discussion of uses of fingerspelling in manual communication
- tips for expressive fingerspelling
- tips for receptive fingerspelling
- tips and exercises for signing numerical information: money, time, addresses and more!
- conversation starters for each unit

ORDER YOUR COPY TODAY!

• •

Please send me _____ copies of FINGERSPELLING THE REAL WORLD at $24.95 each.

Name _____ Date _____

Address _____

City _____ State _____ Zip _____

Phone (____) _____ PO# _____

Total amount of order   _____

*Shipping   _____

Total amount enclosed   _____

*Shipping: $3 for the first book and $1 for each additional book.

Early Intervention Works!
Infants and Toddlers Can't Wait

Write to them)

real world
Press
P O Box 47193

**The Virginia School for the Deaf
and Blind @ Hampton**